PRECIOUS
in His Sight

OTHER BOOKS AND AUDIO BOOKS
BY JODI MARIE ROBINSON

A Royal Guardian

PRECIOUS
in His Sight
Seeing Yourself As God Sees You

Jodi Marie Robinson

Covenant Communications, Inc.

Published by Covenant Communications, Inc.
American Fork, Utah

Printed in the United States of America
First Printing: August 2013

19 18 17 16 15 14 13   10 9 8 7 6 5 4 3 2 1

ISBN-13: 978-1-62108-469-3

Dedicated to my precious jewels—
Christian, Jacqueline, Sydney, Cody, and Zoey

ACKNOWLEDGMENTS

I AM GRATEFUL TO THE wonderful team at Covenant who has made this book possible. My words are so much better with your vision and fine-tuning. To Kathryn Gordon, who gave me my first opportunity to publish *A Royal Guardian*, thank you for believing in that story, which has led me to other writing opportunities. My heartfelt thanks goes to my editor, Samantha Millburn, who believed in this book from the get-go! I recognize her expertise and talent and know that when I am working with her, I am in excellent hands.

To my husband, who years ago gave me a laptop so I could write whenever and wherever I felt like it, thank you for supporting my hobby, even though it won't ever afford you a villa in Italy or early retirement! To my children, who listen to me read my chapters out loud, I appreciate your patience and constant cheerleading. To my in-laws, Rich and Suzanne, and all of my extended family, thank you for sharing my books with your friends and neighbors. To my grandma Baker, thank you for buying up all of my books the first day they hit the store! To my dear friends who, years ago, encouraged me to write—thank you for believing in me. To the ladies at House of Hope, my second home, you are my life teachers and inspiration and continually make me want to be a better person. To my loving mom and dad, thank you for teaching me that I am precious to God and for loving me unconditionally so I can in turn love others.

Thanks to anyone whose path I have crossed who has given me experiences to write about. My potpourri of "wisdom" is because of all of you. And finally, to my readers—if I could encourage you to believe in one thing, it would be to never doubt how precious you are to God. And remember: believing it is one thing, but living like you believe it is even more precious.

TABLE OF CONTENTS

INTRODUCTION

NO GREATER HAPPINESS EXISTS THAN knowing who you are and understanding that you matter. Knowing that the almighty God cherishes and loves you at all times, even when you think you are the least lovable, is a priceless gift.

I remember sitting in a chair next to my grandparents' rock fireplace when I was eight and my father placing his hands on my head to give me a father's blessing. Although memory fails to recall the exact words, the feelings I had during and after the blessing were unforgettable. I was young, but I could feel that God knew who I was. That experience has affected my life for good in the decades that have followed. I felt it then. And I feel it now.

No longer a little girl, I have continued to ask God that same question— Do you know me? *Not* because I doubt but because I love being reminded of it over and over again. I love knowing that I am precious to Heavenly Father, that He knows me by name and sees my true worth. Every time I ask for His reassurance, the answer comes. Sometimes it comes through an experience. Sometimes it comes when I read a scripture or listen to a talk, lesson, or song. Other times it comes as a still, small voice that relays peace and joy to my heart. And it makes me blissfully happy.

What I did not understand at eight years old is that hard things happen in life. Dashed hopes and shattered dreams sometimes knock a girl down. Hurt and disappointment can make it difficult to see God, let alone feel Him, and hard things make it easy to wonder, *Does God even care?*

His happiness is based on bringing "to pass the immortality and eternal life of man" (Moses 1:39). His children's eternal happiness is His sole purpose. That does not mean, however, that our lives will be trouble free 24/7. The eternal happiness Heavenly Father offers us depends on our eternal spiritual progress. As we faithfully recognize and learn to be totally reliant on God's vision of who we really are, we align ourselves with Him and feel His happiness more prominently in our lives. Holding tightly to the knowledge that God deems us His precious daughters will anchor our souls to the straight and narrow course that will lead us back to Him. There is no other way.

Discovering we are precious to God is a continuous, unchanging, eternal gift—one worth opening again and again. I hope that as you read this book, you too will feel the deep love Heavenly Father has for you and come to know, without a hint of doubt, that you are precious to Him. If you happen to already know this deep inside your heart, then let it encourage you to share what you know with someone who needs reminding.

With love and friendship,
Jodi

The most precious jewels are not made of stone, but of flesh.

—ROBERT LUDLUM

God sees you as precious.

CHAPTER 1
The Ruby Secret

*She is more precious than rubies: and all the things thou
canst desire are not to be compared unto her.*

—Proverb 3:15

WHEN I WAS YOUNG, MY father owned a jewelry store. It was located in a
busy downtown shopping mall and had rows and rows of glass cabinets
filled with lavish and expensive jewels. On display were diamonds, pearls,
sapphires, emeralds, and, of course, my favorite—rubies! I remember
pressing my hands against the glass and admiring those bright red stones
tucked inside delicate black velvet boxes. Even looking at them gave me a
thrill.

For my tenth birthday, I begged my parents for a ruby ring. The
moment I saw a black velvet box sitting next to my pink-frosted cake, I
knew my wish had come true. I pulled back the lid to discover a thin gold
band mounted with a tiny ruby, not a monstrosity of a stone by any means.
In fact, it was barely the size of a single piece of birdseed. But size didn't
matter. It was a real ruby. And it was all mine!

At the ripe old age of ten, I certainly was not a ruby expert. In fact,
my expertise began with "They're pretty" and ended with "They're sparkly."
Looking back, I can't even explain what caused me to love rubies so much,
nor did I have any inkling that my tiny stone held a remarkable secret. I
later discovered that its secret completely changed the way I saw myself
and everyone else around me—forever.

Although it has been said secrets should be kept and not shared, this is
not one to be kept from others. In fact, the more this secret is shared, the
better.

I call it the "Ruby Secret."

❦ ❦ ❦

I discovered the Ruby Secret by accident, although that should not make it any less important. After all, some amazing discoveries have been accidental, like the discovery of penicillin, potato chips, Post-it Notes, Silly Putty, corn flakes, and even the microwave and fireworks. For fireworks, the story goes that in tenth-century China, a cook accidentally mixed up a concoction to cure meat that resulted in a colorful combustion. What a wonderful surprise it must have been to see bursts of colorful fire popping into the air!

The night I accidentally discovered the Ruby Secret, one could say I experienced spiritual fireworks of my very own. Nothing that night was out of the ordinary. I was in my routine of reading the scriptures before bed when a random verse in Proverbs caught my attention—chapter 3, verse 15, to be exact. It was a quiet night. The kids were asleep. My husband was working late. All lights in the house were off except the cream-shaded lamp on my nightstand. As soon as I read that verse, it was like a sparkler lit up inside me: "She is more precious than rubies: and all the things thou canst desire are not to be compared unto her."

Who is *she*? I wondered.

And what exactly makes whoever *she* is more precious than rubies?

Intrigue then led me to ask the obvious questions: Why rubies? Why not diamonds or pearls or some other precious gem? And why was *she* more precious than they?

I grabbed my laptop, and with the click of the mouse began an intense search to find out all I could about rubies. Into the night, with a light streaming across my computer screen, I read page after page about rubies: where they are found, how they are mined, and what makes them so valuable. I discovered some basic facts that, surprisingly, shed light on the possible meaning behind that scripture:

Fact number one. Rubies are categorized as *precious gems*. By Webster's definition, something that is *precious* is "valuable," "highly esteemed," or "cherished." But in the gem world, to be categorized as precious, a gem must also be rare.

A ruby is all of those things. And it is extremely rare. In fact, for thousands of years, the ruby has been considered one of the most valuable and rare gemstones on earth. Monarchies have been threatened and wars have raged to obtain them. Most rubies are found in Mogok, Sri Lanka, a small island in Southeast Asia. It is considered to be the ruby capital of the world. On that tiny isle, ruby mines cover about four hundred square miles; however, only seventy of those four hundred square miles actually bear gems. Imagine *all* of that land, and still, natural rubies are found on less than a quarter of it. What does that tell us? It tells us that even in the ruby capital of the world—the bedrock of discovery—rubies are exceptionally rare.

Fact number two. Rubies are made from a mineral called corundum, the same mineral from which sapphires are made. Sapphires are also considered precious gems, but a sapphire is blue, and a ruby is red.

These two distinctly different colored gems come from the very same mineral, but a slightly different amount of this mineral can produce an entirely different gem altogether, leading me to believe that a ruby is not a ruby by chance but is destined to become one.

Fact number three. Chromium is the element from which a ruby attains its deep red color, often referred to as pigeon's blood. The more chromium the ruby has, the deeper the color red. And in most cases, the deeper the color red, the more valuable the stone. There is, however, a downside to chromium: it causes cracks, or fissures, to form inside the stone. And these cracks cause rubies to break into smaller pieces, making them less valuable. It is a delicate balance between having just the right amount of chromium to produce a nice red color and having too much and causing considerable breaks and cracks.

The saying goes that diamonds are a girl's best friend because when a man gives one to a woman, he is making an investment in her. But it goes without saying that finding a substantially sized ruby with few imperfections or impurities happens so rarely that when it does happen, it brings a hefty price at auction—even more than a diamond, sometimes five times as much! In fact, substantially sized rubies with such high quality and clarity that they have few cracks are *so* rare and *so* costly that you'd have to be royalty to afford them.

What does all of this have to do with you and me and the secret? Let's go back to Proverb 3:15, which states, "She is more precious than rubies: and all the things thou canst desire are not to be compared unto her."

Now that you know a little more about rubies, who is verse 15 talking about?

Who is *she*?

That quiet night in my bedroom, with the lamp light streaming across my Bible, my fingers tapping my laptop keys, I received an answer to that very question: "*You*, Jodi Marie. That is who this scripture is talking about. That is how God feels about *you*."

That means the *she* is also *you*.

And what does verse 15 say about you? That you are more precious— *more* precious!—than rubies. And rubies are one of the most cherished, highly esteemed, exceptionally rare, and most sought-after gems in the world.

Finding a perfect or near perfect ruby is nearly impossible, and when a ruby of such high quality is found, it costs *more* than even a diamond, a gem held in the highest regard all over the world.

That is how precious you are!

God could have declared you—His precious daughter—to be *as* precious as rubies or *almost* as precious, and that would have still meant you were something very special.

But He didn't do that. Instead, God declared a woman's worth—your worth and my worth—to be *more* than one of the most valuable and rare of gems—ever! And to top it off, God did not stop there. He went on to say that *nothing* can be desired or compared to how precious we really are.

Being precious to Heavenly Father is what gives us true worth. And that is *very* precious.

I can still remember the thrill it gave me to stare at those beautiful red rubies in my father's jewelry store. But today, I thrill in truth. I have something far more precious than those jewels. I know and understand my true worth. I know in the deepest part of my heart—without doubt—that "the most precious jewels are not made of stone, but of flesh."[1]

To God, you and I are more precious than rubies.

That is the Ruby Secret, and it means the world to me.

❧ ❧ ❧

What does it mean to be precious to an eternal and almighty God, a Heavenly Father who rules over this universe with the perfect precision of a wise parent, who loves unconditionally with a fierce devotion that spans millennia, and who desires your eternal happiness beyond your wildest imagination? It means that even on the days when you have dropped the ball, missed the boat, or flat-out made a mistake, you are still precious. Your inherent worth as a daughter of God is unchangeable and irreversible. There is nothing you can do to change the way God feels about you.

He wants you to know how precious you are, and He wants that knowledge to transform who you become. Can you imagine how different the world would be if each and every one of God's children understood that they were precious to Him and acted accordingly? That would change our world entirely.

The Ruby Secret has certainly changed the way I see myself each and every day, in moments of struggle and in moments of blessed gratitude for all that God has given me. It has also changed the way I see all of God's children, increasing the love and awareness I have for them. And as I share this secret and it opens their eyes to who they really are, like the blind man to whom Jesus restored sight, they too can say, "One thing I know, that, whereas I was blind, now I see" (John 9:25).

Being queen is a good thing.

CHAPTER 2
Destined to Be Queen

Ye are gods; and all of you are children of the most High.
—Psalm 82:6

I WAS A QUEEN ONCE, back in the sixth grade when my best friend, Amy Hockenberger, made me queen for a day. The royal treatment began one cold January morning at the corner bus stop as soon as I stepped up onto the curb.

"Hear ye! Hear ye!" Amy blurted out with gusto. "I hereby declare it Queen Jodi Day!"

"Umm. Amy?" I asked as all eyes shifted in my direction. "What are you doing?" Nervously, I stuffed my hands inside my puffy red coat, recognizing that Amy was definitely up to something.

"Hello, Your Majesty." She bowed. Then, without warning, she plopped a pink paper crown on my head and handed me a colorful poster board decorated in giant bubble letters that spelled out words like *nice*, *smart*, *funny*, and *pretty*.

"Amy? What is going on?" I continued to inquire.

"Don't you get it? It's Queen Jodi Day."

Amy could not contain her excitement, and by the looks of it she had been planning Queen Jodi Day for quite some time. Right then, our bus pulled up, and Crash, our driver, opened the doors. Before I could ask another question, Amy spread out her arms, blocking everyone from boarding the bus—except me.

"The queen *always* boards first," she insisted.

Well, for some crazy reason, everyone listened. Including me! Up I went into my giant yellow carriage with my poster board in hand and my pink paper crown bobby-pinned to my head. (I mean, what else was the queen to do?)

Amy followed behind me, busily taping pink crepe paper all around my seat.

"Congratulations!" students said as they passed by.

Like any junior-high student trying to avoid undue attention, I half hated it and half loved it.

Once we got to school, Amy explained that being royal meant she would carry my books to class, open my locker, and sit by me at lunch. And the best part was when she gave me a chocolate candy bar between English and social studies. Students and teachers chuckled at my homemade crown but seemed obliged to support the clever charade. I still can't believe I wore that silly thing. But you know what? The absolute truth is—it felt good to be queen.

Later that day, I asked Amy why she had made up a Queen Jodi Day. And she said she had noticed that I had been acting a little down in the dumps and that she figured making me queen might just cheer me up.

Now isn't that the sweetest thing a best friend could do for you? She wanted to make me feel special. And it worked. Thirty-some-odd years have passed since I was queen for a day, and I still smile every time I think of Amy Hockenberger and my pink paper crown. Amy and I have not seen each other in years, but I'll never forget her and how she made me feel. I hope life has treated her kindly and that those around her have treated her like royalty. After all, being queen is a good thing.

❧ ❧ ❧

In God's eternal plan of happiness, we as faithful daughters of God were made for more than pink paper crowns. We were made to be real queens.

The question is, do we live to claim this eternal blessing? Or in our day-to-day goings and comings, do we lose sight of that eternal truth and live beneath our privileges? Right now, as I look around my bedroom, I see obvious evidence that I'm living a less-than-royal existence. Strewn across my royal quarters are at least six lime-green Nerf pellets left over from my son's Nerf war with the neighborhood kids, one flip-flop, four Barbie dolls, a jump rope, and two pairs of dirty socks conveniently located next to an empty box of Cheese Nips—evidence that someone unlawfully ate in my bed while watching a movie. Sleeping in cracker crumbs is not a very queenly thing to do. Then, out my window (which just happens to be covered in hard-water spots), dandelions are sprouting up in my back lawn even after I doused them with a very expensive and poisonous weed killer that should have worked weeks ago. And then there is my smelly black cat, a skinny stray I inherited in a weak moment, that keeps jumping up on my lap.

Is there anything seemingly royal about what I just described?

Not really, which leads me to surmise that sometimes being queen is hard to imagine.

It's kind of like when the boy who asked me to the senior prom decided to get back with his girlfriend one week before the dance and left it up to my friends to inform me that he was no longer taking me. Yes, that happened, and I sure didn't feel like a queen then.

I am fully aware, after living more than four decades, that singing bluebirds do not fly into my window each morning to match the endless socks in the overflowing sock bin, and elves do not sing me to sleep at night when I am feeling anxious about my seemingly endless to-do list. And my royal carriage, up until recently, was the equivalent of a decade-old white minivan with a cracked bumper and the permanent smell of chicken nuggets and fishy crackers inside. Oh, how I wish I could believe there is no such thing as no-show princes and that everything in life turns out nice and neat like a perfectly harmonized finale in a high-school musical.

But I can't because this is mortality, a prelavish existence where royal hopefuls experience heartbreak, mistreatment, and disappointment that knock their crowns right off their noggins.

But—and there is a big but—even though life gives us sour notes here and there, a royal inheritance awaits, and as far-flung as it seems, it is never out of reach. With an eternal perspective, the royal blessings of eternity can and will be realized.

❧ ❧ ❧

Having an eternal perspective means trusting that God will make good on His promise to *someday* make us queens. It means having faith in His eternal plan of happiness and trusting that He deems His spirit daughters to be more precious than rubies despite their cracks and fissures and regardless of life's tosses and turns.

This promise is found in a beautiful scripture in John 14. It is posted on my bathroom mirror to remind me every day to hold tightly to that royal perspective, even when I am having a bad hair day (or worse). It states, "Let not your heart be troubled. . . . In my Father's house are many mansions: if *it were* not *so*, I would have told you. I go to prepare a place for you" (John 14:1–2). Those beautiful words are a promise from our Savior, Jesus Christ to every daughter of God that we are indeed queen material. Notice the word *many*. Many mansions are in my Father's house. That means there is a mansion with your name on it. Mansions are not just for perfect people, because there are *many* mansions in our Father's kingdom, even mansions for those whose lives mimic a royal mess rather than a royal fairy tale. This promise provides great comfort and peace.

He who is perfect will not and cannot make a promise He cannot keep. He laid down His life so you and I (who are not perfect) could become queens. Jesus Christ willingly wore a crown of thorns so you and I could wear crowns of glory.

Let us go back for a moment to picture this scene. Jesus's angry accusers placed a crown of thorns on His head as they led Him to His place of crucifixion. They spat on Him, mocked Him, and whipped Him, and still, He walked to Calvary, carrying the very cross on His back to which they would nail His precious hands and feet. Jesus could have refused that crown of thorns. He could have stopped everything from happening. But instead He wore the crown willingly. And He did so with His thoughts turned to you and me and to all of the sons and daughters of God who desire to live as kings and queens in the eternities with God the Father.

I believe that crown of thorns is an important part of the Savior's matchless gift to us—His infinite Atonement—without which none of us could ever qualify to receive an eternal crown of glory (see 1 Peter 5:4). Without it, we would be locked in our sins and kept from God's presence. Jesus's crown of thorns is a holy symbol of royalty because it represents sacrifice. And it is surely the crown that makes Jesus Christ our king.

So if ever you doubt or wonder if you are queen material as you survey your less-than-royal existence, remember that One far greater than you or me wore a crown of thorns, and He did so to ensure that the daughters of the King would receive mansions in their Father's kingdom. We must sacrifice whatever we are asked to here and now with humility and grace and embed the gift the Savior has given us deeply in our hearts and minds.

❧ ❧ ❧

Can you picture it? Your mansion?

It is beautiful.

And it is yours for all eternity because the Savior went to prepare a place for you in it. This promise is eternal. It is for me. It is for you. It is for every daughter of God, no matter who she is or where she lives—even if she has never been queen for a day.

Choose your crown wisely.

CHAPTER 3
Giving Up Earthly Crowns

For after [she] hath filled the measure of [her] creation, [she] shall be crowned with glory, even with the presence of God the Father.

—D&C 88:19

IN LIFE, WE ARE TESTED to see what kind of crown we want most. There is a parable from the New Testament that teaches us this lesson. In it, a rich young man asked Jesus, "Good Master, what shall I do to inherit eternal life?"

Jesus replied, "Thou knowest the commandments, Do not commit adultery, Do not kill, Do not steal, Do not bear false witness, Defraud not, Honour thy father and mother."

And the man answered Jesus saying, "Master, all these have I observed from my youth."

"Then Jesus beholding him loved him, and said unto him, One thing thou lackest: go thy way, sell whatsoever thou hast, and give to the poor, and thou shalt have treasure in heaven: and come, take up the cross, and follow me." When the man heard this, he was sad and "went away grieved: for he had great possessions" (Mark 10:21).

At a closer glance, we find that this parable is not really about riches; it is about earthly crowns. The man wore a crown of riches, which defined him. It looked good on him and looked good to others. It turns out he was so comfortable wearing it that he decided to hang on to it even if it meant he could not follow the Savior. It's where he got his validation. I would hope that if Jesus were standing in front of me, I would eagerly say, "Here, take my earthly crown. I don't want it. I'm coming with you." But apparently, from reading this story, we learn that it is not that easy. And I believe this parable's purpose is to remind us of that—that giving up earthly crowns is often hard to do. If we take a closer look at this parable, we find out why.

Perhaps what this man *had* was who he thought he *was*, and, as Dr. Phil would say, this man felt like his crown was working for him. He was probably well liked and cherished because of it. In his eyes, his wealth was what made him precious. It was what gave him worth. And if our worth is tied up in our earthly crowns, imagine how hard it will be when we're asked to give them up. We might worry about who and what we might become without one.

We should be able to empathize with this man as we come to see ourselves in him, because at some time or another, we too have worn an earthly crown that, for whatever reason, was hard to give up, even though we knew deep down it did not fit our desire to follow Jesus Christ.

And we occasionally wear different types of crowns. Some give us a sense of belonging and importance. Others give us a sense of superiority. Some crowns define who we think we should be, while others define who we want others to think we are. We wear some crowns as a consequence of sin after having given in to worldly temptations. And some crowns are decorated with pride, self-centeredness, entitlement, and vanity. Some of us may even wear a martyr's crown.

King Benjamin warned of the diverse ways we can commit sin. "For there are divers ways and means, even so many that I cannot number them. But this much I can tell you, that if ye do not watch yourselves, and your thoughts, and your words, and your deeds, and observe the commandments of God, and continue in faith . . . even unto the end of your lives, ye must perish" (Mosiah 4:29–30).

We might not think of perishing when we think of putting on our favorite crown, but that is exactly what happens. Our spiritual well-being weakens when we choose earthly crowns over heavenly ones. There are times we are just like the man in the parable. We rationalize that the crown we currently wear fits so nicely with our lifestyle that we don't know why we would want to give it up. We reason that it has become such a comfortable way of being that it would be too hard to wear a different one. And the truth is, we happen to like who we are when we are wearing it, and our friends like us when we are wearing it. Our fears of what would result if we took it off and exchanged it for a crown of sacrifice and duty and commandment-keeping keep us locked up. Other times, we worry that our mistakes have made us unworthy to dream of ever wearing a crown of glory, so why not just keep the one we currently have?

Regardless of the reason we have chosen to wear our earthly crown, just like the man in the parable, we have to remember we are given a choice—the choice to give it up and be with Christ in that mansion on high or walk away grieved and be separated from the Savior. It is a choice we must make. Like the rich man, we might be doing a lot of right things, but that earthly crown we wear, the one we have come to like so very much, is the one thing holding us back. And God knows it. He is waiting for us to give it up so we can enjoy a full relationship with His Son, Jesus Christ. It could be a way of dressing, a way of spending time, a way of speaking, a way of treating someone, a way of eating, a way of spending money, a way of earning money, a way of thinking about our bodies, a habit, a hobby, or a relationship. It could be any number of things. It could even be an addiction. For twelve years, I have taught motivational classes to women recovering from substance abuse, and I can say that the crown of addiction is one of the hardest to give up. And yet, I see women do it against all odds and enjoy the blessings of full recovery and a lifetime of sobriety. I am amazed by their bravery and conviction to choose something better even when change seems hopeless. From these beautiful women, I have learned that nothing is impossible to give up if a relationship with the Savior is what we desire most.

So the question is: what do you desire most?

❧ ❧ ❧

You cannot give up your earthly crown until you identify what it looks like. And Christ can help you do that. Go back to the parable. Remember how Jesus looked inside the man's heart? The scripture says, "Then Jesus beholding him loved him." To *behold* someone is to discern the whole person, to really see inside their heart. We know Jesus saw all of this man, his strengths and weaknesses, his hopes and fears. That is why Jesus could identify what the man was lacking and could tell him what he needed to do to change.

Christ does the same for you and me. He beholds us, and He loves us. As we go to Him in earnest, seeking prayer and ask Him to help us identify our earthly crowns so we can give them up and be with Him, He helps us. And He blesses us. The Savior gives not as the world gives but as God gives (see John 14:27). He wants us to exchange our earthly crown for a different kind of crown—a crown of righteousness.

In D&C 25, we are taught, "Behold . . . thou art an elect lady, whom I have called. . . . . Walk in the paths of virtue. . . . Lay aside the things of [the] world. . . . Cleave unto the covenants which thou hast made. . . . Keep my commandments continually, and a crown of righteousness thou shalt receive." A crown of righteousness is one that never tarnishes or loses value, a crown that sparkles with the most glorious blessings of eternity, a crown that qualifies sons and daughters of God to be in the presence of the most high God. That holy crown is the one the Lord wants to give you should you desire to have it.

⁊⅊ ⁊⅊ ⁊⅊

Now let us go back to the parable to consider yet another aspect of its teachings. I like to think that this is not the end of this man's story because that means it is also not the end of our story. Let us imagine that after this man leaves Jesus, he decides to spend some time thinking about what Jesus has asked him to do. And let us suppose that as he ponders the things in his heart, he has a desire to change his mind. Maybe after some heartfelt consideration, prayer, and pleading with Heavenly Father, he decides to find Jesus to tell Him he wants to follow Him after all. With a grateful heart for the patience and understanding Jesus has shown him, humility then washes over him. His pride dissipates, and self-worth swells within his heart with such intensity that he desires to fulfill the true measure of his creation—to be more like Jesus (see D&C 88:19). And let us imagine this man comes to an understanding of what Jesus is asking him to give up for his spiritual and eternal well-being. Christ is asking him to give up something of little value for something of greater value. And because he chooses to do so, he is no longer weighed down by weakness. His only desire has become to receive a crown of righteousness.

"I no longer have a need to wear my earthly crown," the man would say. "My only need is to be like you, Lord." What a beautiful ending to that parable!

Our story can have a similar ending if we choose it, no matter how our story began. Christ knows the shape of our crown. He also knows what we need to do to give it up. I am certainly not preaching this because I have mastered it; I still have a long way to go. But as I teach the ladies at House of Hope, we all learn to become who God wants us to be. And learn I can.

I am counting on Christ to remove and repair my weaknesses as I honestly and diligently work on giving them up. You see, Christ wants to make us queens. I get that. He wants to crown us with righteousness. But

He can't unless we are willing to break up with the world, take up our cross, and completely give Him our hearts. It does not work to wear an earthly crown on weekdays and a heavenly one on Sundays. It doesn't work to rationalize that wearing a certain type of crown is not so bad, that everyone is doing it and there are worse things in comparison. That is exactly the kind of thinking that keeps our earthly crowns perched atop our heads.

To wear a crown of righteousness, our hearts must be set on sacred things. Things not of this world. And to receive a crown of righteousness and enjoy the blessings of eternal life with God the Father and His Son, the crown we must seek and desire above all others is jeweled with the sacred, holy, and godly works we do here on earth. There is nothing earthly about it.

I pray that when Jesus Christ asks each of us, "Will you give up your earthly crown and come follow me?" we will be the kind of women who eagerly answer, "Yes, I will."

You were created for greater things.

CHAPTER 4
Created for Greater Things

[She] went about doing good . . . . for God was with [her].
—Acts 10:38

SEVERAL YEARS AGO I WAS serving as a Relief Society president in Texas. One evening the bishop called and asked me to visit a woman who had just arrived from Africa on a temporary work visa. Her name was Susan, and I was told she was converted to the Church in her village in Uganda after two missionaries taught her the gospel. She was staying with her uncle at an apartment complex near my home, so I went to visit her the next morning.

I knocked, and a man opened the door and motioned me in. He spoke with a pleasant accent. Moments later, a tall, thin woman about my age appeared in the doorway of a back room and then walked gracefully toward me.

"Hello, my sista!" she said as her long arms wrapped around me.

I could not help but love her instantly. After all, Susan *was* my sister because the gospel made us family.

Susan and I talked for a few minutes about finding her a job. The bishop told me she had come with only the clothes on her back, so we also had some shopping to do. As we drove along Grapevine Highway, she told me about her two children back in Africa: Paul and Rebecca, who were nine-year-old twins. She had plans to secure their visas and bring them to the States to live with her as soon as possible. I was in awe that she could leave them but learned that she had not had much choice. To give them a better life, it was a risk she felt she had to take.

Life in Susan's village had been hard—so different from the life I had known living in America. In talking with her, I learned that under the previous dictatorship of Uganda's past leader, Idi Amin Dada, whose nickname was "Butcher of Uganda," Susan had witnessed unspeakable violence and savage massacres. Many members of her family had been tortured and killed, and because of her ties to family members who had rebelled against Idi Amin, she was afraid if she returned she would be hunted and killed. Her village was poor, but she left her children in the care of a neighbor, all the while fearing that they were being taken advantage of and that the money she was sending her children to go to private school was being used wrongfully. That later proved to be true.

Stepping through the automatic doors of the giant discount superstore, Susan gasped in disbelief. It was like watching a kid see Disneyland for the first time. I never knew Walmart's wide aisles and overstocked shelves could evoke such delight.

"So much of everything in one place!" Susan exclaimed as she eyed the rows of food and clothing.

Her smile stretched as far and wide as the African continent from which she had come. As she ooed and awed over the merchandise, my heart teeter-tottered with guilt. I shopped at Walmart weekly and had never been that excited over ten different kinds of antiperspirant. For me, filling my basket to the brim was as ordinary as turning on running water in my kitchen sink, which, by the way, for Susan, was a luxury.

After checking out, I handed Susan her plastic sack containing under-wear, shampoo, soap, deodorant, a toothbrush, and toothpaste. You would have thought I had given her a diamond ring. She was incredibly gracious. Next, I drove her to my house for lunch. As we turned onto my street, she cautiously studied every home.

When I pulled into my driveway, she asked me a strange but serious question. "Sista Joti? Is this *your* house?"

She pronounced my name *Joti* with a *t* instead of a *d*. It sounded so regal, and I loved it! She stared out the window, tipping her head back so she could see the top of the second story. By American standards, my home was nothing special, certainly nothing to go googely over. In fact, it was considered a modest starter home. Nothing about it was luxurious, especially the peeling paint on the shutters. I explained to Susan that my husband and I had lived in an apartment for five years until our first daughter, Jacqueline, who was contentedly sleeping in her car seat, was born.

"Joti?" Susan reached for my arm. "Are you a princess?"

"What?" I said smiling and half laughing.

But Susan was quite serious. The next thing she said to me took me by complete surprise. "*Joti* . . .where I come from . . . this house is what a princess lives in."

My heart jumped into my throat. I honestly could not speak. I didn't know what to say. I found out later that the conditions Susan and her twins had been living in were deplorable. They had been living in an eight-by nine-foot room with the roof caving in and mice running rampant, and there I was living in a two-story house on Canterbury Street in the middle of the Dallas metroplex, with convenient access to every nationwide retail superstore chain, a debit card, credit cards—or, in other words, access to everything I ever needed. It turns out—I was a princess.

I learned quickly that Susan was a woman who believed Jesus Christ when He told her there was a mansion in heaven with her name on it, even though all she had in her possession at that moment was a plastic sack full of toiletries. In the two years I knew her, Susan exemplified the gospel principle found in 2 Corinthians 4:8, which says, "We are troubled on every side, yet not distressed; we are perplexed, but not in despair." I watched her suffer disappointments as she held on to hope, waiting for her children to get permission to join her in the States. Even when getting her children seemed impossible, Susan pushed forward. She worked hard at her job at the local grocery store. I will forever remember sitting in my kitchen, holding my baby in my lap, with pennies, nickels, dimes, and quarters strewn across the pine table, teaching Susan how to make change so she could pass her cashiers' test. I can still hear her voice. "Thank you, Joti. Thank you for teaching me that a dime is worth two nickels."

To raise money to get Susan's kids here, I organized a fundraising garage sale with my dear friend Mindy, who came to love Susan just as I did. The three of us spent a lot of time together over the next nine months going to lawyers and learning everything we could about political asylum. Susan reminded us that where much is given, much is required. And getting her twins to Texas required a lot—a lot of faith and a lot of patience.

After two long years, with the help of a determined lawyer, Susan received the rare gift of political asylum, which meant she never had to go back to her homeland. I will never forget her phone call shortly after her court hearing in Galveston, Texas. She was wading in the Gulf of Mexico with Mindy (splashing around, actually), and they were celebrating.

"I am free, Joti! My children are coming! God is good!"

By the time mother and children were reunited, they had been separated for two years. The only contact Paul and Rebecca had had with Susan was through faxes, letters, and monthly phone calls, and even then, sometimes she couldn't get through. Can you imagine being so far away from your children for two whole years? I can't imagine living without my children for a week! (Okay, I'm stretching. My youngest just called my middle child a name, and my third oldest just complained about tonight's dinner menu. I could go a week without seeing them and still be okay.) But two whole years in which I couldn't see them grow, couldn't hug and kiss them? Susan had to be so brave!

What I love about Susan's story is that life before coming to Texas was anything but ideal, and when she got here, it was still really tough. But that didn't stop her from being a good person, raising good children, and loving God. Deep in her soul, she knew enduring hard things was only temporary. She truly believed she was created for something greater.

Believing you are created for greater things is a big part of the Ruby Secret. We don't really belong here. Earth is our temporary home. As I write this chapter, a song plays on the radio that conveys that message. Country singer Carrie Underwood's voice pleads for us to see that in this life we are just passing through temporary windows and doors, and my heart leaps because in that simple song is a truthful message.[2] The song may not be meant to convey the depth of the eternal message we as Latter-day Saints know to be true, but we do believe we are journeying on to something better. "For our light affliction, which is but for a moment, worketh for us a far more exceeding and eternal weight of glory; While we look not at the things which are seen, but at the things which are not seen: for the things which are seen are temporal; but the things which are not seen are eternal" (2 Corinthians 4:17–18). In the premortal world, we agreed to live in mortality temporarily to work out our "own salvation" (Mosiah 9:27). That is part of God's eternal plan of happiness.

We live in perilous times. In speaking to the young women of the Church in 2011, then general Young Women President Elaine S. Dalton described our temporary world as "ever growing in moral pollution, tolerance of evil, exploitation of women, and distortion of roles."[3] But, even so, great things are in store for those who show royal courage, who guard and seek the faith, and who believe there is such a thing as being made for greatness in the kingdom of God.

❧ ❧ ❧

Sadly, I lost track of Susan after I moved from Texas to Utah. Mindy and I have tried to find her, but after she received political asylum, she moved to a different city and stopped going by her last name. Last I heard, Paul and Rebecca were doing well in school. They would have graduated from high school by now, perhaps even starting families of their own. I hope and pray that I will one day have the privilege of seeing Susan and her children again. But until then, I hope she remembers how special she is and that she is a princess of the divine kind.

What is lost can be found.

CHAPTER 5
Remember to Remember

Oh, remember these words, and keep my
commandments. Remember, this is your gift.

—D&C 8:5

I ONCE LOST MY PRECIOUS wedding ring. I looked everywhere for it—in my closet, behind the nightstand, under the bed, inside pockets, purses, and pillows, but it was nowhere to be found. After eight months, I gave up hope of ever finding it. Then one morning as I was cleaning out the cabinet under my bathroom sink, I picked up a jar of jewelry-cleaning solution and was about to throw it in the trash when I felt prompted to look inside. Thankfully, I followed that prompting. Would you believe that there, at the bottom of the jar, resting inside a white, plastic tray was my ring? And it was sparkly! I was one lucky girl. Had I thrown out that jar, my precious ring would have been lost forever.

Finding something precious requires special help. And I believe at the right time, that help comes from God. Like when I lost my ring, God helped me find it by helping me *remember* what I already knew but had forgotten. I had bought the jewelry cleaner while shopping with my mother. I was pregnant at the time (need I say more?). My fingers were starting to swell, and my brain was starting to shrink. I completely forgot that I had decided that jar would be a good place to keep my wedding ring during the months I could not wear it. Because using cleaning solution was not something I was accustomed to doing, and because pregnancy hijacks my brain and shrinks it to the size of a pea, I forgot what I had done with it until God helped me remember. At a crucial moment, God helped me recall important information that helped me recover something very precious.

ɞ ɞ ɞ

Like my precious diamond ring, sometimes *we*, who are precious, get lost. Life's challenges and experiences, sometimes outside of our control, cause us to forget the plain and precious truths that remind us how precious we are—and when this happens, we end up giving in to lesser things.

The most important part of the Ruby Secret, once you discover it, is to remember it. *Never* forget it. The word *remember* is used 136 times in the Book of Mormon, 144 times in the King James Bible, 40 times in the Doctrine and Covenants, and once in the Pearl of Great Price. Do you think God is trying to tell us how important it is to *remember* what we have been taught by saying *remember* over and over?

And just what have we been taught?

For starters, we have been taught that we are daughters of God, made in the image of God. How many times have you heard or sung the song "I Am a Child of God"? How many times have you recited the Young Women theme that says you are a daughter of Heavenly Father, who loves you and you love Him? This theme is repeated every week in Young Women. In the Relief Society declaration that hangs on the wall of every Relief Society room are the words "We are beloved daughters of a Heavenly Father."

Why these words?

I believe these words, more than any other words that could be expressed, are there for a reason because remembering who we are and how precious we are is so very important to God and to our salvation.

Sister Dalton once told a story about the son of King Louis XVI of France. It is one of my favorites and is an excellent reminder of how important it is to remember who you are.

Wicked men captured King Louis and tried to overthrow his kingdom. They also kidnapped his son, the prince. The kidnappers thought that "if they could destroy [the prince] morally," he would never realize the great and grand destiny that life had bestowed upon him. These men took the prince far away from his father's kingdom and exposed him to every vile and lewd temptation known to man. But even though the prince was young, he did not buckle under pressure. He remembered who he was and told his captors, "I cannot do what you ask, for I was born to be a king."[4]

How different the world would be if each daughter of God, whenever tempted to give in to lesser things, would respond, "I cannot, for I was born to be a queen."

ᘒᕽ ᘒᕽ ᘒᕽ

Do you remember *you* were born to be a queen? Do you remember *you* were born for greatness?

The world is full of people who do not understand what it means to be a daughter of God and why remembering that eternal truth is so important. The adversary's temptations to give in to lesser things are real. Opportunities to live beneath our privileges come at us from all sides. But the key to *not* being tricked into giving into lesser things is to *remember* who you are at all times, in all things, and in all places (see Mosiah 18:9). Just like the prince, we must never deny what our spirits know to be true.

Remember.

Hold tightly to the eternal truth that to God you are more precious than rubies, and shake free of any influence that is contrary to that teaching. Never surrender. Be true to God, in whose image we are made.

ᘒᕽ ᘒᕽ ᘒᕽ

President Dieter F. Uchtdorf has said, "Much of the confusion we experience in this life comes from simply not understanding who we are." Without the belief that you are more precious than rubies, life will be confusing. It will be like looking in a mirror and not recognizing your own reflection. In a fireside at Brigham Young University, President Uchtdorf retold the popular story of the ugly duckling, where a swan mistakes her identity for a duck. It is not until she looks into the water to see her reflection that she understands who she truly is. He concluded:

> Think of where you come from. You are . . . daughters of the greatest, most glorious being in the universe. He loves you with an infinite love. He wants the best for you. . . . This knowledge changes everything. It changes your present, it can change you future. And it can change the world. . . . There will always be voices telling you that you are foolish to believe that you are swans, insisting that you are but ugly ducklings and that you can't expect to become anything else. But you know better. . . . You are no ordinary beings. You are glorious and eternal. I plead with you, just look into the water and see your true reflection.[5]

Have you seen your true reflection lately?

In my family room, I have a mirror. On it are vinyl letters that say, "Always remember who you are." Looking in that mirror, with those words staring back at me, I remember who I am and what choices I need to make because I know who I am. Those words are there to remind me when I turn on the television or listen to the radio. They are there when I gather my children around the table for scripture study. They are there while I am surfing the Internet, reading a book, or talking on the phone. They are there when I am headed out the door, and they are there when I return. That saying is there to help my family and me remember who we are and where we came from because remembering those two things is so very important.

To remember who you are every second of every hour is a small and simple thing upon which great and important things depend. And God knows that. So He does everything He can to help you remember.

Not long ago, I was in a hurry to get across town, and I seemed to hit every red light. My frustration increased with each stop. It was my own fault for leaving so late, but still, I had much left to do, and this particular errand could not wait. When the light finally turned green, I pushed on the gas. As my car picked up speed, I looked up ahead and noticed something unusual. Someone had taken red plastic cups and decorated the chain link fence on the overpass up ahead. Of all things, it spelled out the word *remember*. I pushed on my brakes, slowing down long enough to safely stare a little longer. Someone had gone to an awful lot of trouble to put that word up there, and I wondered who it was for and for what reason. Someone wanted someone else to remember something.

It seems we spend so much of our time hurrying from here to there that we forget to look up and sometimes end up focusing our attention on the wrong things. We hurry off to school. We rush to work. We dash off to practice and scurry through the grocery store. We check our e-mail, update our status . . . and find ourselves forgetting. Before long, our perspective gets clouded in the dust of day-to-day living.

When I placed my wedding ring in that jar of cleaning solution, my perspective was on track. I was safekeeping something precious. But what happened over time? I forgot. All of my efforts to keep my precious ring safe could have been for naught had I carelessly thrown out that jar and made a decision in haste. It was a very good thing I slowed down long enough to listen to that voice help me remember, or I would have lost something precious.

Slowing down, being still, pondering scripture, attending Church, going to the temple, meditating, and praying—these are all things that help give us an eternal perspective and help us remember who we are so we do not lose sight of what is most precious.

❧ ❧ ❧

So, what if you have forgotten?

With a little help from Heavenly Father, you can remember how to remember who you are and how precious you are. Maybe you are good at remembering but your teenager needs a little reminding. Or the sister you visit teach. Or the friend you have not spoken to in quite some time. Here are some scripture treasures to help us remember. They are the first place I go whenever I am feeling a little forgetful.

You are a child of God (see Genesis 1:27).

You are so valuable to God that even the very hairs of your head are numbered (see Matthew 10:29–31).

Heavenly Father knows everything about you (see Psalm 139:3).

He knows when you sit down and when you rise up, and He even knows your thoughts before you think them (see Psalm 139:2).

Heavenly Father knew you before you were conceived (see Jeremiah 1:4–5).

You are of more value than the sparrows (see Luke 12:7).

God numbers all things, for they are His, and He knows them all (Moses 1:35).

Even if you forget a million times each day, God will never tire of reminding you how precious you are to Him. He loves reminding His daughters how precious they are. And He is reminding you right now. Listen to the Spirit testify of this truth, and remember what it feels like to be reminded, because it feels wonderful!

❧ ❧ ❧

Whenever I look at my precious wedding ring, I remember what I almost lost, and I am once again forever grateful for that still, small voice that helped me remember. God glories in helping us remember we are precious. So when He reminds you, listen.

God loves all of you.

CHAPTER 6
Every Part of You Is Precious

Even the very hairs of your head are all numbered.

—LUKE 12:7

THE SUMMER AFTER I GRADUATED from high school, I boarded a plane and headed for college, two thousand miles away. At the end of my first semester, I flew home to see my family for Christmas break. Two weeks of vacation passed by quickly, and I enjoyed shopping, ice skating, eating dinner at my favorite Italian restaurant, and hanging out with family and friends. Before I knew it, I was back on campus. Shortly after arriving in my dorm room, I received a phone call from my mom, and I'll never forget what she said. It was the oddest thing. She said, "Jodi, I just found one of your curly brown hairs in the bathroom sink . . . and I cried for two hours. I sure miss you." I missed her too, but honestly, I was thinking maybe she should lay off my Italian grandmother's wine cookies because that just seemed weird!

As odd as it was to hear that my mom was crying over my hair strand left in the sink, I got it. It was her way of letting me know how much she loved me and that to her, every part of me was precious. Before hanging up the phone, I told Mom I loved her and that summer would be here faster than she could say "second semester break."

Well, many years later, a funny thing happened. My oldest daughter was leaving home for the first time to go to girls camp, and you will never guess what happened. After she left, I was cleaning the bathroom and found a piece of her curly brown hair in the bathroom sink . . . and I cried! I couldn't talk to my daughter because she was at camp, so I called my mom to tell her how much I was already missing my Jacqueline and how precious she was to me.

❧ ❧ ❧

Now, let us take a look at this thought on a grander scale.

The scriptures teach us that to God, "even the very hairs of your head are all numbered" (Luke 12:7). What is the significance of this? Why is numbering all of the hairs on your head important to God? I cannot say for sure whether or not Heavenly Father would cry over hair in the bathroom sink, but I do believe this scripture is teaching us an invaluable lesson. Heavenly Father wants us to know something very important—that *every* part of us is precious.

God loves *all* of you! From your eyelashes down to your toenails, He sees marvelous perfection. When He looks at you, He does not complain and say, "Oh, I'd like you better if you had fuller lips and caramel highlights." That never enters His mind.

God loves you just the way you are and would never disparage any physical characteristic you have or don't have and wish you were different. In fact, He cares so much about *every* part of you that He goes so far as to number the very hairs on your head. This scriptural teaching is paramount to women! It is so important for you and me to understand this principle that God put it in a scripture. And to me, that is just beautiful.

❧ ❧ ❧

If we're being honest, woman to woman, sister to sister, girlfriend to girlfriend, we have to admit that loving all of ourselves is sometimes hard to do.

Why is that?

Studies report that when looking in the mirror, "8 out of 10 women will be dissatisfied with their reflection, and more than half may see a distorted image."[6]

Oh, how I detest those words—*dissatisfied* and *distorted*—and I have a strong feeling that our Creator and Maker does too. To feel dissatisfied or to allow beliefs about our bodies to become distorted is to deny the godliness that is in us. Our bodies are gifts from God. And yet, according to research, women feel unhappy with their reflection because they see an image that, by worldly standards, is imperfect and, therefore, never good enough.

A big reason for this dissatisfied and distorted view of our physical bodies is media. You may already know that most images seen in magazines, on the Internet, and on television are retouched, airbrushed, and digitally enhanced to imitate an unrealistic standard of beauty. A popular software program called Adobe Photoshop can change an image in a single click. Bosoms, buttocks, thighs, arms, waists, brows, elbows, and necks are enhanced, diminished, cinched, trimmed, elongated, manipulated, and artificially recreated. Yes, ladies, beware! No body part is beyond being digitally dissected. It turns out *no* part of a person is off limits when it comes to reshaping the human body. And isn't that just sheer nonsense when you stop to think about it?

As it turns out, even babies' photos are retouched to meet a standard of attractiveness.

A recent documentary exposed that "babies' eye color, skin tone—and even the fat creases on their arms—are altered before the images are put on glossy magazine front covers."7

Airbrushing babies? It is just plain *nonsense*. Having had four babies of my own, I can think of nothing more perfect than a baby's velvet skin and lovable fat rolls, and yet, for some reason, there exists in our society a standard that requires alterations to ensure a more physically appealing look, like trimming folds of fat to somehow make a baby cuter.

Instead of getting sucked into this media insanity, we must become media savvy and recognize that our society's ever-growing fascination with the quest for the idealized and perfect physique is not where a daughter of God's focus should be. We must not be deceived.

As Sister Elaine S. Dalton expressed in the October 2008 general conference: "Could it be that we have been deceived by false role models and persuasive media messages that cause us to forget our divine identity? . . . What could be more deceptive than to entice women, young and old, you and me, to be so involved in ourselves, our looks, our clothes, our body shape and size that we lose sight of our divine identity and our ability to change the world through our virtuous influence?"8

We cannot afford to spend an endless amount of time choosing hobbies and interests that do not give us a solid return on our eternal investment. How we spend our time will determine who we become.

We can choose to show the world a better and happier way, a way of living that springs up with lasting happiness, not counterfeit joy. We know better. We know who made us. We know where we came from. And we know what we're worth.

How can we make a difference in a media-saturated society that teaches that a woman's worth is in her looks? First, we can be honest. No one is unaffected. As I pass by billboard after billboard on the freeways, even I become desensitized. But what I know at my core is that what I look like is not for sale. God made me. He is my Creator. And my less-than-perfect parts do not lessen my value. I refuse to be deceived.

Second, we can get real. We can talk honestly and candidly with each other, with our daughters, with our sons, and with our husbands about how it feels knowing that women are being picked and poked at, chiseled and carved like we're specimens in a laboratory, all in an effort to make us fit some picture-perfect Barbie doll image that is not real. And the truth is, it doesn't feel good. It hurts physically and mentally. Beauty is found in the miracle of creation. And creation is God's work. We are His handiwork—*that* is the truth. That is what feels right. It is what makes daughters of God beautiful! To pretend otherwise is blasphemy.

We may not be able to change society entirely, and I think we're headed in a direction where these distortions are only going to intensify; however, we can refuse to be deceived. We can rebel against the lies that we're only worth something if we look a certain way. Messages that make these kinds of claims will always exist, but we don't have to believe them or even listen to them. We have the power to shape opinion by example and show the world where true worth comes from because of who we are and what we know and the powers we possess as heirs to God's kingdom. We can teach true principles of worth by example. We can be that light on the hill for all the world to see, as Jesus taught in the Sermon on the Mount (see Matthew 5:14). Others will see our beauty and notice our happy ways.

True beauty does not come from an airbrush. It comes from an inner belief that God numbers the very hairs on our heads (whether we have a full head of hair or not). If we want to change how we see ourselves and how others see us, we must see ourselves as God sees us. We will like ourselves more than ever before. And we will discover that others do too.

A woman I know is on a mission to lose one hundred pounds. She came to see me with her daughter at a recent book signing and brought me a chocolate cupcake. I teased her that she was clever to give the cupcake to me so she could eat it vicariously. When she told me about her goal to get healthy previous to this encounter, I cheered her on and reminded her to commit herself to healthy choices and to let God be her coach. He would transform her.

Committing to make lifestyle changes that support healthy eating and exercise are worthy spiritual goals. So are furthering education, increasing talents, and learning new skills. If you have changes to make, make them. If you need to be more healthy, do it for this reason: your body is a gift from Heavenly Father. Be moderate in your choices. Make healthy life-style choices that fit within gospel teachings. And you will shine!

It is true you may not like all of you *all* of the time. And looking at the airbrushed images in magazines, billboards, and Internet sites isn't going to help you like your body any better. So stop looking at them. Don't pay them any attention. Studies show that if you're looking at the media as a source of inspiration, you will actually like your body less.[9] I suggest looking at images in the media as little as possible. Consider them your kryptonite; kryptonite drained Superman's powers, and that is exactly what false images of perfection do to daughters of God who are trying hard to remember who they are and that they were created in the image of their Father.

Identical twins Lexie and Lindsay Kite devoted their PhD studies at the University of Utah to women and the media. They are the founders of the not-for-profit Beauty Redefined Foundation, and their slogan is "Take Back Beauty!" They are studying the representations of female bodies in popular media. I like that they encourage women to be intentional about how they view their bodies to avoid being emotionally swept into a sea of unrealistic ideals that lessen a woman's self-esteem. In terms of media images, they suggest logically evaluating what we are looking at and how it makes us feel. "If these images and texts motivate you to respect your body . . . make and reach fitness goals, and maintain health that will keep you happy and able, then they are appropriate for you. If they motivate you to worry about being looked at or to improve parts of your body to meet a beauty ideal you see in media, you must be aware of this."[10]

I applaud Lexie and Lindsay because they say, "We can begin to realize it is the standard that needs changing—not us. We should never feel like our bodies are some sort of burden to bear instead of a precious gift we've been given!"[11]

Like Lindsay and Lexie, I am committed to taking back beauty. Are you? They suggest doing simple things to make your voice heard, like refusing to shop in stores where images of women are exploited as objects; writing letters to store management or posting on social media to express opinions; sticking Post-it Notes on the images themselves that say "Take back beauty" to indicate you have a voice and you want to be heard; becoming educated and informed about the negative effects media can have on self-esteem and how to reverse it.

Those are just a few ways we can be heard. Lindsay and Lexie's website, www.beautyredefined.net, is full of empowering ideas and well-documented research. They won a top paper award for their work dealing with women self-objectifying themselves in popular lingerie ads in the Women's Studies division at the National Communication Association Conference in New Orleans in November 2011. Nationally, they have stepped onto the stage and are saying what a lot of women want to say but won't. They are getting us talking, and I think it's wonderful. I'm all for standing up and sharing my belief that women are worth *more* than their parts! We are worth more than rubies.

If for any reason you are struggling to love all of your pieces, I would encourage you to read this next chapter carefully because I know of a remedy that will help you love your body, and I am willing to bet all the Hershey bars in the Northern Hemisphere that you will agree with me. But before I share it, I want to tell you story.

You are going to have sideburn moments.

CHAPTER 7
Sideburn Moments

*And he said unto her, Daughter, be of good acomfort: thy faith hath made thee
whole; go in peace.*

—LUKE 8:48

WHEN I WAS A TEENAGER, a boy too cute for words told me something
no girl ever wants to hear. He told me I had . . . okay, here goes—he told
me I had sideburns.

Could you just die?

Oh, sure, I can laugh about it today. But back then, sideburns seemed
like a fatal blow. I mean, he just blurted it out while we were walking to
class one day as if he were announcing what was on the lunch menu. No
big deal, right? Wrong. It was completely nightmarish. Sideburns are cool
if you're a fifteen-year-old *boy* but *not* if you're a fifteen-year-old girl! I
was humiliated. I wanted to race out the front doors and join the Lady of
Lourdes Catholic convent on the other side of town and never see that boy
(or any other boy, for that matter) ever again.

After some initial contemplating, I realized the convent thing was a little
far-fetched. When my mom picked me up after school and tried making
small talk, I nearly didn't hear a word she said because I was busy scheming
and silently begging God to punish boys who told girls they have sideburns
by cursing them to never grow their own. As soon as we pulled into our
driveway, I bolted out of the car, raced upstairs to my mother's medicine
cabinet, and secured a bottle of Nair hair remover.

In today's beauty market, there are hair removal products for different
kinds of body parts, from earlobes to ankles, but when I was a teenager,
there was pretty much only one kind—the leg kind. I was convinced,
however, that it was the only way to eliminate my problem. I locked the

bathroom door and, bottle in hand, glanced briefly at the directions. I slathered the lotion on my face and waited. After several minutes, I noticed a slight tingling feeling. A burning, actually. But determined to rid myself of this awful curse, I pressed on. Apparently, fifteen minutes was a little *too* long because when I washed the lotion off and looked in the mirror, to my horror, all I could see was two bright red stripes, one on each side of my face!

Oh, I had side*burns* all right. And I could feel them.

As it turns out, sideburn moments (as I now call them) lend themselves to learning invaluable lessons, and I would like to share a couple of the lessons I've learned with you.

Through that sideburn experience, I learned I had two really good friends who were kind enough the next day not to question why my hair was styled differently, all brushed toward my face. The real, powerful, life-changing lessons, though, were the ones kept close to my heart. Lessons I have remembered each time my self-esteem has taken a hit.

Lesson One: *Only listen to voices you can trust.*
When hit with a sideburn moment, you should first go to a parent, spouse, trusted friend, leader, or person of integrity, someone who cares about you and believes your worth is found in being a daughter of God. When that boy told me I had sideburns, I should have gone to my mother before diving into the medicine cabinet to burn off my face. I should have been brave enough to tell mom what that boy had said to me and how crushed I was and how ugly he made me feel. I could have trusted my mom with my true feelings, and had I gone to her first, she would have helped me put things in perspective. Perhaps our conversation would have gone something like this:

"Jodi Marie, don't you listen to that silly boy. You don't have sideburns, and even if you did, you'd still be the most beautiful girl in the world. You are prefect just the way God made you. You have beautiful brown eyes and curly brown hair. And you try so hard to do what is right. You sing and dance and are a good sister and friend. Don't waste one single second listening to nonsense. And by the way, who is this boy, and where does he live? I'm going to call his mother and give her a piece of my mind!"

Thank goodness Mom never made that call. But I admit that it feels good knowing she would have had she known what had happened and if I had needed her to. My mother loved me. And more importantly, she knew God loved me. And if sideburns were really a problem that would hinder my personal development as a lovely daughter of God, I guarantee she would have suggested a better option than a hair-removal lotion that burned off my face. *Together*, we would have found a suitable solution to deal with sideburns.

Sharing sideburn moments with someone you trust is key to maintaining a strong self-image. What is the definition of someone you trust? It is someone who loves you, but even more importantly, it is someone who knows how much God loves you and who believes you are more precious than rubies. If you are currently listening to *any* voice that speaks contrary to the criteria we've discussed—*stop* listening to it immediately, because you can't trust it. Voices disconnected from God don't have your best interest at heart. In my case, a fifteen-year-old boy was not a trusted source. And more often than not, magazines, TV commercials, billboards, Internet sites, a radio announcer, or anyone who says you would be better if you were different— no matter how convincing they might be—are not trusted sources.

Disreputable sources do not acknowledge the meaning of being more precious than rubies. Some sources are just interested in your pocketbook. The beauty industry is a multibillion-dollar business. If you don't think green stuff is important to a company that promises you more self-confidence if you buy what they are selling, think again. There are many facets of the beauty industry, and the adversary has been able to manipulate some of them to fit his plan in order to confuse, distract, and deceive daughters of God and stop them from reaching their eternal potential. He is constantly campaigning to get women so caught up in the chase for worldly beauty that they miss eternity entirely.

Being persuaded to try a fuchsia lip gloss is pretty harmless, but too often, media messages are much more persuasive and manipulative and send us spinning in the wrong direction. Be careful what you buy in to. In the thesaurus, the word *manipulate* is synonymous with the word *fool*. Don't be fooled by listening to false sources that try to sell you self-worth. Worldly places and pursuits, where the focus is primarily on the outside and not the inside, are *not* trusted sources. Never trust them with something as precious as your self-worth.

Lesson Two: *Only Christ can restore and repair sideburn moments. Only He has the power to heal. And when it comes to sideburn moments, healing is what you need.*

Perhaps the most important lesson I learned from my sideburn moment (and many others since) is the importance of healing. It is important to decipher what you really need when your self-image takes a hit. After my sideburn moment (besides wanting to give that boy a fat lip), I was fooled into thinking I needed a "quick fix." However, my problem could not be fixed by a bottle of lotion. I didn't need Nair. I needed healing. And I am not talking about the healing salve I could have used to soothe my self-inflicted side*burns*. I'm talking about the healing power that comes through the Atonement of Jesus Christ.

You may be as surprised as I was to find out that the Atonement covers sideburn moments—but it certainly does. Heavenly Father knows how important it is for His daughters to have a strong self-image, and He is prepared to help every daughter of God feel good about herself no matter what her ailment may be.

You don't like your knees? God has a solution for that.

You don't like your elbows? God has a solution for that too.

You may have other parts that you feel are less than desirable, but God has a solution for every part of you!

So how do I know the Atonement works for sideburn moments?

Because I have experienced it.

As silly as it seems to talk to Heavenly Father about sideburn moments because, let's be honest, God has so many more important things to worry about than a girl who has sideburns, we can rest assured that these issues really are important to Him.

There is nothing so inconsequential that God does not care about it. God happens to number every hair on your head, and through His Son, Jesus Christ, He restores everything to wholeness. Fixing what is broken is Jesus's job. Healing what hurts is His mission. And when a sideburn moment happens to a daughter of God, Christ's genuine love and concern can cover you like a warm blanket the minute you pray to Heavenly Father and ask Him to heal you.

Since that first sideburn moment, I've experienced many others. And each time I have asked Heavenly Father to help me see myself through His eyes, He has healed me. And then He does more amazing things for me. He strengthens my heart so much that He gives me the desire to help other daughters of God see themselves as more precious than rubies.

True healing through the Atonement is the best kind. You will come to love and appreciate your body, sideburns and all, as you never thought you could because you will see what Heavenly Father sees. You will be inspired to take care of your body physically and spiritually and treat it as the beautiful gift it truly is.

Oh, how I wish I could tell my sweet daughters there are no such things as sideburn moments. But I can't. Sideburn moments are going to happen. They may come from a comment, a photo, a thirty-second commercial, a tweet, or a post. I can't stop them from happening. But when they do happen, I can promise this: you can trust your Heavenly Father and His Son to heal you.

You can experience the same kind of power used to heal that "certain woman" in scripture who suffered from a blood disease for twelve years. This woman was probably an outcast, considered to be unclean even among her own people. Can you imagine how little self-worth she must have had, spending all her days seeking out physicians and remedies that never worked? She must have felt extreme hopelessness. But then one day, something inside her awakened. She mustered up enough courage to wander out into the crowded street where Jesus was walking with His disciples. Throngs of people pressed against Him as He made his way through the crowd, and she drew close enough to touch the hem of His garment (see Luke 8:43–48). Jesus felt her touch, and when He turned to ask who had touched Him, His disciples responded, "Master, the multitude throng thee and press thee, and sayest thou, Who touched me?" (Luke 8:45). In other words, it could have been anyone. There were so many people in the streets that day. But Jesus knew. He knew who had touched Him. He knew the woman who had touched Him, and He knew she had done so seeking to be healed (see Matthew 9:21). The scriptures say Jesus felt "virtue" leave Him (Luke 8:46). He knew the difference between someone brushing up against Him and someone coming unto Him for healing.

"And [Jesus] said unto her, Daughter, be of good comfort: thy faith hath made thee whole; go in peace" (Luke 8:48).

Notice the word *whole*. To become whole is the perfect definition of healing. And this "certain woman" was made whole.

You too can be made whole if you exercise faith in the Lord Jesus Christ. Remember to include the Savior in whatever self-improvement program you are following. Seek healing as you seek to improve whatever is making you feel less than whole. And don't be afraid to ask for it. Have the courage to talk to the Savior and ask Him to heal you. Even if you're broken up over silly sideburns, if your desire is to be made whole, Christ will give you peace. And who better to give it than the author of peace—the only begotten Son of the Eternal Father—a God who loves you so much that He just happens to number every hair on your head.

❧ ❧ ❧

When the world tells you you aren't beautiful, remember that God loves *every* part of you. Because of that first sideburn moment, I discovered the marvelous truth that there is healing, even for silly sideburns. And to me, that is precious.

Only God can determine your worth.

CHAPTER 8
The Worth of Your Soul

The worth of souls is great in the sight of God.

—D&C 18:10

A WONDERFUL SEMINARY TEACHER NAMED John Hill taught me a principle of self-worth in such a profound way that it changed me forever. I had just finished speaking to a group of mothers and daughters at a stake Young Women conference when Brother Hill, also the stake president, was asked to conclude the meeting. He stood at the pulpit, adjusted his suit jacket, opened up his scriptures, and asked, "What is the worth of your soul?" Then, in silence, he waited.

Immediately, I answered that question in my mind: *The worth of a soul is great! Doctrine and Covenants 18:10.*

After a long pause, Brother Hill leaned into the mic and asked the same question a second time. He waited a few seconds and then read the verse I had thought of: "Remember, the worth of souls is *great* in the sight of God." He emphasized the word *great*. And then he said loudly, "But . . . that is not the true worth of your soul."

What? I questioned. *The worth of a soul is great in the sight of God. That's the scripture, so where is he going with this?* I wondered.

He continued.

"The *true* worth of your soul," he explained, "is found in the verse that immediately follows verse 10. It is there that we find the worth of a soul. Read verse 11 with me. 'For, behold, the Lord your Redeemer suffered death in the flesh; wherefore he suffered the pain of all men, that all men might repent and come unto him.' In other words, your soul is worth . . . the life . . . of a God. You are worth the life of a God. That is the true worth of your soul."

Wow! I had never thought of it in that exact way before. It was a priceless teaching moment for me. The way he said it completely changed the way I see my own worth and, hopefully, the way you see yours.

ꝕ ꝕ ꝕ

Do you look at your worth in that way? That your soul is worth the life of a God? Do you see that your worth has everything to do with Jesus Christ—a God who bled from every pore in Gethsemane and surrendered Himself to the cross on Calvary? Can you fathom the reality that the life of a God was given to save your soul? It seems incomprehensible, but in order to understand true self-worth, you must comprehend what this means to you personally.

Everyone wants to feel a sense of worth. Deep down, everyone wants to know they matter. Feeling loved, valued, and cherished is what every human being wants to feel because when we feel those things, we feel whole. Our souls were meant to be loved, valued, and cherished. God made us that way. We began as His cherished daughters, and deep down, we remain so. Keep in mind, though, that there is a difference between being loved, cherished, and valued for temporal things and being loved, cherished, and valued for eternal things. When you base your self-worth on temporal things—things that can change, like looks, money, achievements, and possessions—your self-worth constantly changes. But when you base your self-worth on eternal things—things that are permanent, like how God sees the worth of your soul, an eternal truth that is the same yesterday and today—your worth remains steady and constant despite life's ups and downs. This is a big part of the Ruby Secret—understanding the true worth of your soul.

Far too many sons and daughters of God base their worth on their looks, money, and achievements—temporary fixes in the scheme of life— not understanding the dangers of that kind of worldly thinking. Worldly thinking separates us from God's eternal love, and when we are separated from God's love, we cannot feel His love or His Spirit. And if we cannot feel God's love and influence, we will fail to feel our true worth, which, as daughters of God, is the only thing that can really make us happy and help us make correct choices that will lead us back to Him. Knowing the true worth of our souls is the only thing that will inspire us to live up to our divine potential.

⅔ ⅔ ⅔

Two years ago, after one of my firesides, a young woman came up to me and said, "I don't feel God's love." Her eyes seemed to pierce the floor. The way she dressed and how she carried herself indicated that she was having trouble remembering she was a beloved daughter of God. I was so touched that she would share such personal thoughts with me, a stranger, that I hugged her. She told me my presentation on the beauty of virtue really helped her and that I had given her some good things to think about. As I listened to this sweet girl, my heart swelled with love. I knew I could not fix her life. I could not make choices for her or changes for her. All I could do in that moment was wrap my arms around her and testify to her that I knew God loved her, that she was more precious than rubies, and that if she would turn to her Heavenly Father, she would feel His constant, life-changing love and be able to accomplish the things He needed her to do. I told her I believed with all my heart that Heavenly Father wanted to show His daughters their true worth; He just needed them to go to Him and ask Him to lead them to places and give them experiences where they could come to believe it for themselves.

Later that night, on my way home, my mind was fixated on this girl. I thought about other young women who might be questioning their worth and how easy it was to just give up and give in. I drove down the freeway and noticed that off in the distance, I could see the Jordan River Temple. Just beyond that temple, I noticed the Oquirrh Mountain Temple. And up ahead in the other direction, I could see the Draper Temple. And I thought, "Why is it that sitting in our midst are three of God's holy temples and so many still end up questioning their worth?"

Why do we question how precious we are?

Remember Sister Elaine S. Dalton's question: "Could it be that we have been deceived by false role models and persuasive media messages that cause us to forget our divine identity? . . . What could be more deceptive than to entice women [to] lose sight of [their] divine identity and [their] ability to change the world through [their] virtuous influence?" The adversary's influence is real. Sister Dalton and many other wise leaders have given fair warning, reminding us that giving in to the deceptions of the adversary is not what daughters of God do. The adversary's influence pulls us away from God's love (which is the only source of true self-worth) and pushes us toward the world's deceptions and lies about a woman's worth. The mists of darkness settle in subtly. It is hard to notice them at first, but they soon cloud our judgment and our ability to see clearly. Worldliness in all forms steals away pieces of us, but we must protect ourselves, especially our souls. They are precious and are the part of us eternally connected to our Father in Heaven, who created us. We must guard them at all times and in all things and in all places.

Many years ago, Elder James E. Talmage told a story that illustrates this idea perfectly. He talked about two thieves who broke into a safety vault to steal a treasure of enormous wealth. The thieves knew the massive vault of steel was constructed to be burglar proof, but they were determined to break in anyway. With drills, saws, and explosives tempered to penetrate even the hardest of steel, the thieves tried with all their might to open the vault. They underestimated how difficult it would be to saw and drill through steel, but they kept at it and eventually got through. When they finally reached the interior of the lock, they forced open the massive doors, expecting to see drawers filled with diamonds, rubies, and pearls. Instead, Elder Talmage explains, they "encountered an inner safe, with a door heavier and more resistant than the first, fitted with a mechanical lock of more intricate construction. . . . The metal of the second door was of such superior quality as to splinter their finely tempered tools; try as they would they could not so much as scratch it."[12]

Your soul is protected by a treasure vault, and only you hold the key. Worldly and evil influences cannot gain entrance to your heart or soul without your permission. Without an invitation to enter, evil influences are rendered powerless. You decide what gets in and what stays out. So when negative thoughts of self-doubt or worldly impressions hold your mind hostage, lock them out. Start with something simple: say a prayer, sing a hymn, recite a scripture.

One of my favorite scriptures is found in D&C 84:88: "I will be on your right hand and on your left, and my Spirit shall be in your hearts, and mine angels round about you, to bear you up." I can think of a time when this scripture brought me peace during a difficult trial that seemed almost insurmountable. It was the light I needed to get me through, and I said it over and over, day after day, week after week until the darkness passed.

Prayers, hymns, and scriptures are simple but powerful things that invite the Spirit. With the presence and positive influence of the Holy Ghost, you will feel peace in your soul no matter how dark the mists appear.

Another way I have come to feel peace when conflicted is to picture the Savior standing by me. In this picture, my family is standing with the Savior.

He looks life-size, as if He is standing right by us. It is a large painting hung in the visitor center during the Draper Temple open house before the temple was dedicated. I love this picture! It reminds me that Jesus Christ will stand guard. He will guard your soul if you let Him.

Robinson Family
Draper Temple Open House 2009

The Savior counsels us, "Watch and pray, that ye enter not into temptation: the spirit indeed is willing, but the flesh is weak" (Matthew 26:41). Protect what is precious by remembering always that your soul is great in the sight of God. So great, in fact, and so precious that it is worth the life of a God.

A mighty change makes all the difference.

CHAPTER 9
A Mighty Change

In me ye might have peace. In the world ye shall have tribulation: but be of good cheer; I have overcome the world.

—John 16:33

AT WINTER'S END, I SURVEYED a flower bed next to my house. It was overgrown with dead bushes and plants left over from the previous summer. I had neglected to cut them down at the end of the season, something perennials require for suitable regrowth in the spring.

I pulled and snipped until my bucket overflowed with dead branches and leaves. As I cleared away the remaining pile, I noticed green clusters peeking through the soil. Changes in seasons had beckoned the vegetation to do what it was created to do—grow. I was the gardener and simply needed to make room for new growth.

I slipped off my work gloves, leaned over, and ran my fingers across the newly revealed foliage. Despite my neglect, these plants were ready for change.

Just like those plants in my flower bed, growth and change are our destiny. The Master Gardener provides opportunities for growth and change and makes us more suitable for His kingdom.

Even when the soil we are planted in feels rock hard and we feel like we are hidden behind lifeless vegetation, a mighty change awaits just beneath the surface.

❧ ❧ ❧

With the deadline fast approaching for the final editing of this book, I had a prompting to add one more chapter. For weeks my pages remained empty. Then I heard about a woman named Al Fox, a convert from Rochester,

New York, who blogs at www.alfoxshead.blogspot.com. She openly shares her experiences about becoming a member of The Church of Jesus Christ of Latter-day Saints. In March 2013, Al was featured on the cover of *LDS Living* magazine and in the *Deseret News*. She was tagged as the "tattooed Mormon." Her story intrigued me, so I e-mailed her and asked if I could interview her. She said yes, so we met for lunch.

Al met the LDS missionaries in 2009. At first, she said she was happy and not looking for God. The elders, as she put it, were getting a little annoying, so to get them off her back, she made them a deal: if the clean-cut, white-shirted missionaries would bring her a steak dinner, she would promise to read their book. The elders brought steak, and Al read their book.

"I always keep a promise," she said.

Unexpectedly, Al loved what she read. She said the Book of Mormon taught her that God valued her soul and her eternal salvation enough to provide a Savior for her. She needed to do her part. She knew bad habits had to be left behind. It was a journey, but in time, changes came.

After her baptism, she wrote to the mission president and told him, "I feel anxious more than anything else. Anxious to tell my story, anxious to talk about everything I have learned, anxious to teach what I know from my experiences. Anxious to motivate and inspire others."

Despite the reservations of friends and family, she packed up and moved to Utah. Converts obviously do not have to move to Utah, but Al wanted to be around more single adult Mormons, so she fearlessly made the move to somewhere she had never been. Her growing season had begun.

On her first day in Utah, standing in line at Café Rio, she heard a man say to her, "It's ironic to see a girl that looks like you holding that book." She was holding a Church book . . . and her arms and legs were covered in colorful body art.

"I turned to this man and introduced myself," she said. "I shook his hand, smiled big, and simply said, 'I just got baptized; this is my first day here!' I said it with happiness. I said it with pride. With confidence."

Al explained that she had a choice: to choose to be offended or to share her story and use it to help others. She chose the latter and refused to let anything, including sneers and stares, stop her from enjoying the gospel. She explained to me what she explains to anyone who will listen: that she walked out of her past. That man didn't know her story—that she had left New York, her home, her friends, and her family. She left everything she knew to find out what Heavenly Father had in store for her, and she discovered, like Nephi of old, that God would not build her a boat but that He would teach her *how* to build one. He also gave her a kind and understanding heart for the purpose of creating a safe passage between past mistakes and future successes.

God is definitely helping Al build something. He is allowing her to tell her story to tens of thousands of people so they can learn how a soul can be transformed. Her "mighty change" (Alma 5:12–14) compels her to talk, blog, and make videos about it. She has cleared away the old branches of her past life and is making space for new growth. She wants people to get past the red, green, and orange swirls on her arms and get inside her head and heart. She is building bridges of understanding and paving the way for others to follow her example and walk back into the arms of Jesus Christ.

❧ ❧ ❧

Forgiveness and repentance—these are essential gospel principles. They clear the way for new growth and are prerequisites to making a mighty change. Like Al, we must come out of the world, leave it behind, and find new peace in gospel living.

We must also earnestly embrace others seeking forgiveness and repentance.

Are you ready to embrace those ready to be embraced? To not judge?

To make a mighty change, we must move past judgment and into understanding.

How do we do that righteously?

How *do* we judge like Christ?

I think of the woman taken in adultery. Do we stand with the crowd, holding a rock in our fist, ready to throw it at someone we do not understand? Or do we choose grace and kneel down in the sand next to Jesus and beg for the woman's release?

I have done both. I have felt the sting of making a premature judgment and releasing that rock into the air, listening as it thudded to the ground, only later to feel remorse as the Savior gently corrected me. I have also felt the sweet embrace of the Savior blessing me with great joy as I have reached out to welcome those who have felt rejected and dismissed.

Who am I to judge another when I also walk an imperfect road? We need to imprint that thought in our minds and hearts and let that change who we are and how we love others. We need to let people change. We need to provide a safe, happy place for them to do so, knowing that we too are imperfect and need space for grace.

Something as simple as not judging a book by its cover and giving someone a chance can open up a conversation and lead a person to Christ. That is what women who know who they are must do!

This spring, my family was in Moab, Utah, hiking at Arches National Park. We stopped at a gas station to get drinks. One of the employees was outside smoking, and she happened to be pregnant. I glanced over, and my first reaction was, "What is she thinking being pregnant and smoking?" Out of the blue, a quote I had read popped into my head that said, "Don't judge her. You don't know the storms I have asked her to walk through."

The Spirit pricked my heart and cracked it open a wee bit so I could make a better choice. I went inside to get my drink. By the time I was ready to pay, the woman was off her break and standing behind the register, ready to help me. She smiled and asked how my day was going. I instantly felt acceptance and love for her. I did not know her story and refused to give in to my first inclination to judge her. We had a lovely conversation. I got back in my car, and instead of criticizing her, I said a prayer for her. Tears hit my cheeks as I pleaded with God to watch over this woman and help her in the upcoming months leading to her giving birth.

Think of the boy with the gages in his ears.

The quiet classmate who stands against the wall, staring at the floor, with no one to talk to.

The girl who dresses immodestly.

Get to know them. Invite them to sit with you. Invite them for dinner. Bring them to an activity. Show them and teach them that because you know who you are . . . you also know who they are! They are children of God. And He loves them.

Missionaries find people to teach and bring into the gospel. We must do a better job of embracing them and making space for them and letting them change.

I regret not going after a man who walked through the doors of our church building in Texas years ago. He wore a T-shirt with a cigarette logo on it and came in looking for the bishop. I was sitting on the couch with some other members, and one of the men directed him down the hallway before turning to the group and saying, "The nerve of that man entering the church wearing that!" The man was not very far away down the hall and possibly heard the comment. Minutes later, the man passed by and did not pause to greet us or even look at us. I was so ashamed. I should have been better! I should have shot up off the couch and chased him down to say, "We are so glad you are here. My name is Jodi, and I just moved to Texas. What is your name?"

In our meeting in the bishop's office, I raised my hand and said, "That man who came in today may never again walk through the doors of our church because we failed to welcome him. We need to be better. I want to be better."

Al Fox set an example when a rock was thrown her way. She took higher ground and chose not to be offended. Imagine if she had packed her bags and headed home, never to return. What a precious jewel we would have lost! Thankfully, God had already begun working a mighty change in her that gave her spiritual confidence. She believed she was God's handiwork and that she was worthy of His blessings.

Now she is traveling constantly, doing youth firesides, speaking at Especially for Youth conferences, sharing her conversion story on her blog, preparing to write a book, and changing lives. She did not know at first that she would be given those opportunities but still chose to be brave and have faith that God would stand by her. She put herself out there and chose to candidly show what good news the gospel is for anyone walking away from the past. She will tell you she is not focused on the past because she is too busy focusing on the future.

"I never talk about who I was. I only talk about who I am becoming," she told me.

And there is no shame in that. Only beauty.

What did not make sense to her at her baptism makes perfect sense now: being different is the tool God is using to help shape her mission to help others who want to find their way back to Him. "For he that cometh to God must believe that he is, and that he is a rewarder of them that diligently seek him" (Hebrews 11:6).[13]

The Lord Jesus Christ creates opportunities for change and provides safe passage on the way there. In just such a case, Lehi's family was taken on a voyage across an ocean to a promised land so that change could bring about miracles and bless generations to come. And there are others in our day making that same journey who will bless even more generations to come. Are you standing at the dock with arms open, eager to embrace those willing to come unto Christ? Will you take them by the hand and help them see themselves as God sees them?

To anyone afraid of returning to the gospel or joining because of their imperfections, remember the scriptures are full of imperfect people who learned from their mistakes and changed. The Savior says, "Come!" His Atonement prepares a way for growth and change. No matter where you have been, put it all out there. Do not duck and hide and let your mistakes define you. Embrace what is to come. And put your arms around anyone who needs reassurance and encouragement. A mighty change of heart is waiting to be uncovered. It is worth clearing away the old and making room for the new.

God is waiting.

CHAPTER 10
God's Search Engine

If any of you lack wisdom, let him ask of God, that giveth to all men liberally,
and upbraideth not; and it shall be given him.

—James 1:5

God is waiting for you to ask Him who you are and what He expects of you. But where are you looking for answers?

Just for fun, one afternoon I did an experiment on Google. In a search bar at the top of the computer screen, I typed the question, "What does God want His daughters to know?" Of course, I was not expecting anything to show up, but to my complete surprise, after I clicked enter, an entire list of possible hits popped up. I was dumbfounded. The first hit on the list said, "Gift of worth," and the second said, "Daughters of God." Both hits seemed correct, and I was taken aback, at least for a couple of seconds, until my fingers slipped and I mistakenly hit the space bar. Whoosh! In a split second those hits disappeared from my screen, piquing my curiosity as to how I got those hits in the first place. I clicked on the back arrow then scrambled to type in the same words a second time. To my dismay, the second time around, an entirely different list appeared that was nothing like the first. I then clicked on my history and discovered the reason for those results, which gave me a good chuckle. It turned out that my original search had not been in Google at all. I had typed my question in a search bar within the Google home page that linked directly to the BYU broadcasting website, which just happened to access talks and speeches given during devotionals and campus education weeks at Brigham Young University. I learned something significant from this silly experiment: it is important to use the right search engine to discover who you truly are. These days, you can Google, Facebook, and Twitter all you want, read magazines and watch TV shows to find answers for all sorts of things, but only one source can give you the right answer to these questions: Who am I? What am I worth? Where did I come from? Who do I need to become? Important questions like these must be inspired searches because they affect your eternal destiny. Google won't work for those; you have to go to *the* source, our Heavenly Father. He is the source of all light and truth. He knows us better than we know ourselves because He created us and has been with us since the beginning.

※ ※ ※

It was with Heavenly Father in the premortal realm that we learned about the great plan of happiness in which we would come to earth to gain a mortal body and have mortal experiences. We also learned that we could return to live with God the Father and become like Him. But returning home to Him depended on our remembering that we existed as His spirit children long before coming to earth.

After each of my children was born, I remember feeling a strong connection to God and His plan. Holding those sweet, little scrunched-up newborns in my arms testified to me of the reality that there is a divine nature within each of us that connects us to an eternal, life-giving source, our Eternal Father. Heavenly Father has said, "All things are numbered unto me, for they are mine and I know them" (Moses 1:35).

Using the wrong search engine to discover who you are will not link you to that life-giving source. It might even confuse you, distract you, and disconnect you. If you want to know who you are and who you've always been, just ask your Heavenly Father. He will speak to you. He will testify through the Holy Spirit what your purpose is—not to mention what your true worth is. To get correct answers, you need to go where God is. So how often are you in God's space?

How often are you in His scriptures?

In His temple?

In His place of worship?

In service to His children?

How often do you talk to Him?

God's number-one-rated search engine is called *prayer*. It is available 24/7. You don't have to have high-speed Internet, a fancy cell phone, or a social network to use it. You just have to open your heart, share your thoughts and feelings, and have a mustard seed–sized particle of faith that Heavenly Father hears and answers you.

Several years ago when my husband gave me my first laptop, my father taught me how to videoconference with my sister who lived on the other side of the world. I typed in her phone number, clicked on the video button, and within seconds heard dialing. Amazingly, a live video feed popped up. Albania was eight hours ahead. It was nighttime there, and my sister was already in her pajamas. We chatted back and forth as if we were both sitting at my kitchen table. She even panned her computer around her bedroom so I could see what her house looked like. My nieces and nephew leaned into the screen to say hi. It was so much fun to see them and chat with them when they were so far away. That I could sit at my kitchen table in Riverton, Utah, looking at a tiny red dot at the top of my screen and see live video of my sister from clear across the ocean with absolutely no wires attached to my computer amazed me.

How does wireless work? I have no clue. I couldn't explain it if I tried because I'm a concrete kind of gal. If I can't see a wire connecting point A to point B, I can't explain it. But I know wireless works. Period. It just does. There are intelligent people who get it and know the why, what, and how, but for me it's a matter of trusting that it works and benefitting from it. And so it is with prayer.

I can't explain how prayer works because there are no wires, no tangible connections. Just time and space. I don't know how my thoughts and words get to God, but I know they do. Too many of my prayers have been answered not to believe that. I know prayer works! It worked while I was writing this book, in fact. Here is an entry from my journal for February 12, 2011:

> *Lately, I've been feeling heavy hearted. The last few days have been especially hard. I have been so busy with all of the kids' activities, and Christian has been working extremely long hours. I have felt so alone and exhausted. So last night I crawled into bed with my scriptures. I didn't really feel like reading, but I said a quick prayer asking Heavenly Father to help me feel peace. I told Him how I felt completely invisible, like no one really sees what I'm going through. After a few tears, I opened my scriptures. I didn't have the energy to think of a specific topic to study, so I just let the pages fall open. And guess where they opened to? Page 845 in the Bible. At the top of that page, written in my handwriting, was the word rubies. I had opened to Proverb 31. Of all the places in the Bible I could have opened*

to, I opened to the more precious than rubies page! And I sat there, stunned. How does God know how to do that? How does He know? I hadn't worked on my book in months. I had even fought the prompting to start writing again. And there I was, feeling a little forgotten and invisible. God knew I needed to be reminded that I was not forgotten.

Whenever I feel discouraged, like I'm ready to give up writing and give up creating, something happens to change that. In the moment I decide to reach up to God and ask for His help, what does He do? He gives me a gentle reminder that He knows me, that He is still there, and that I am precious to Him. Even I need reminding! Me! The one who is writing a book about being precious to God! He knows how good it makes me feel when He reminds me that He is there for me! I will never forget what is on page 845 in the King James Version of the Bible. Never! To God, I am more precious than rubies!

⁂ ⁂ ⁂

A favorite quote of mine from Ezra Taft Benson states, "Nothing is going to startle us more when we pass through the veil to the other side than to realize how well we know our Father and how familiar his face is to us."[14]

Wow! That I do believe.

Father in Heaven knows us. I cannot explain it other than to say I feel it deeply. When you doubt that you matter or that you are loved by God, go to Him in prayer. Use His number-one search engine to discover your part in His eternal plan of happiness and imagine all the wonderful possibilities He has in store for you. I promise, if you will use prayer to refine your search about who you are and who God needs you to be, He will listen. And He'll not only listen, He will answer.

Trust the Rock.

CHAPTER 11
Heaven's Window

I am come that they might have life, and that
they might have it more abundantly.

—JOHN 10:10

ROCKS AND RUBIES HAVE A close relationship. Without rocks, rubies would not exist because rocks protect rubies as they develop and grow. One reason rocks are such good protectors is that they don't change much over time. Scientific testing shows that some rocks have been in existence for billions of years with little change, if any; thus the saying goes, "Steady as a rock."

Throughout scripture, Jesus Christ is referred to as the Rock (see Deuteronomy 32:4). He is steady, constant, and stable. He does not change. Malachi 3:6 reads, "I am the Lord, I change not." And Hebrews 13:8 says, "Jesus Christ [is] the same yesterday, and to day and for ever." His character, His teachings, His love and devotion to all of God's children show us that Jesus Christ is the rock upon which daughters of God can rely. He is the one to whom we can entrust our most precious possession—our self-worth.

Christ's teachings protect us against worldly influences that erode souls and weaken spirits. Relying upon the rock of our Redeemer protects against the floods of the adversary. "And the rain descended, and the floods came, and the winds blew, and beat upon that house; and it fell not: for it was founded upon a rock" (Matthew 7:25). If your self-image is founded upon Christ, you will be constant, steady, and stable, able to withstand the evil influences of our day.

So how do you build your self-image on the Rock?

You do the opposite of what the world teaches. Instead of relying on yourself, you rely on the Rock. You rely on His strength.

❧ ❧ ❧

I love this story about a man who is told by God to push against a giant boulder sitting outside his window. God said, "I want you to push against that rock." The man loved God, so he obeyed. Every morning, he got up at dawn and pushed against that boulder. Day after day, he pushed and pushed until he grew tired. Then one morning the man realized something: nothing was happening. As hard as he was pushing, the rock was moving nowhere. His efforts seemed in vain. So the man went to God and said, "I can't seem to make any headway pushing against this rock. I see no progress being made. I give up."

God heard the man and said, "Son, you have been faithful in doing what I have asked. I am pleased with your progress. You may not see it, but you have gained much strength and experience from pushing on that boulder. Your sinews and muscles are toned. Your skin is bronzed from the sun's rays. And your mind is keenly focused on my command. I now release you from your burden, but not because you haven't been able to move the rock. You see, I only asked you to push against it. I never expected you to move it. Moving it is my job. You've done what I have asked you to do. Now allow me to move the rock."

Relying on the Rock means trusting in Jesus and in His greater gospel plan. To *rely on* means "to trust." And so we must trust Jesus Christ as our Savior and Redeemer. He is our everything. Even when we don't believe we're strong enough, smart enough, pretty enough, witty enough, or confident enough, we must remember the Lord didn't ask for our résumé. He asked for our obedience. He asked us to trust Him, to follow Him. Relying on the Rock simply means that we keep pushing. We continue keeping God's commandments. And we keep trusting in His promises, even when that boulder we've been pushing on day and night doesn't move an inch. If we keep pushing, the Lord will move our mountains for us. He may even show us how to climb them.

❧ ❧ ❧

Several years ago, my husband and I took our family to Canyonlands National Park in Utah. We hiked several trails during our four-day trip. On our last day, after a long, hot afternoon, the kids fell asleep in the truck. My husband pulled over to the side of the road and pointed to a sign. Mesa Arch. One half mile. To me, that seemed like fifty the way my body and head ached. I had no interest in getting out of the truck and taking another step. Determined to make one last hike, my husband got out and said he would go first and then come back and sit with the kids while I went. I agreed, thinking that by the time he returned, I would suggest we call it a day and head back to camp. After about twenty-five minutes, he returned and said, "You definitely don't want to miss this one."

Ah, but I really do! I thought as the desert air squelched my enthusiasm.

With a little more coaxing, he convinced me to go. I reluctantly hopped out of the truck and headed up the trail. On the way, I passed several people who said, "It's worth it!"

"It had better be," I silently protested.

After a short while, I stopped at what I thought was the top of the trail, looked around at the vast red-rock landscape, and started to turn back. A woman stopped me and pointed about fifteen yards to my right and said, "You need to go a little farther. Heaven's Window is right up there." Not wanting to be embarrassed by my lack of interest, I thanked her and made a ninety-degree turn. After walking several feet, I neared the edge of the red rock as a massive arch emerged. Through it, I beheld a perfectly framed orange, red, and brown backdrop set majestically against a cloudless blue sky. The scene took my breath away. I understood why it was named Heaven's Window. Through it, I could see everything—the entire Canyonlands National Park. I looked out the "window" longer than anticipated, thinking about what I had almost missed. Back on the trail, with each dusty step, I said a quiet thank you. "Thank you, God, for not letting me miss Heaven's Window. That was the best part of the trip."

Back at the truck, the kids were still sleeping. My husband quickly asked, "What did you think?"

"I can't believe I almost missed it. Thank you for encouraging me to go."

It is through heaven's window that we see what God sees. But too often we miss it. Let us not miss the most glorious part of the journey because we are focusing on the wrong things. Yes, we may grow tired in the heat of temptation. We may become shaken because of trials or because we're trying to be somebody we are not. We cannot get distracted by worldliness because it may lead us far enough off the right path that we will miss heaven's window—finding out who we really are and what we came here to do.

❧ ❧ ❧

These wise words of Elder Jeffrey R. Holland inspire me:

> If we constantly focus only on the stones in our mortal path, we will almost surely miss the beautiful flower or cool stream provided by the loving Father who outlined our journey. Each day can bring more joy than sorrow when our mortal and spiritual eyes are open to God's goodness. Joy in the gospel is not something that begins only in the next life. It is our privilege now, this very day. We must never allow our burdens to obscure our blessings. There will *always* be more blessings than burdens—even if some days it doesn't seem so. Jesus said, "I am come that they might have life, and that they might have it more abundantly" [John 10:10]. Enjoy those blessings right now. They are yours and always will be.[15]

Along our path, there will be turnoffs we are allowed to freely explore. The last thing our Father in Heaven wants to do is force us to heaven. But to those who choose to see blessings instead of brokenness, the promises of eternal life are abundant. I often hear a quiet whisper: *Stay on the path. Claim the choice blessing of seeing yourself as God sees you. It will be worth it. I promise. Remember, God has a mansion with your name on it.*

Elder Jeffrey R. Holland advises us to listen to the Spirit, who is encouraging us to live the gospel fully. He says, "Listen to the words of the Lord. Listen to your leaders. Listen to your parents. Listen to the best that is within you. Above all listen to the sweet, soft, undeniable whispering of the Spirit which will teach you all things, including that what I am saying to you is true. It *is* true. Believe in yourself, and believe in this gospel. Believe that we know what we are talking about, and what we are talking about is how terrific you are and how terrific your life can be if you will live the gospel of Jesus Christ."[16]

Thank you, Elder Holland, because all daughters of God need to know they are terrific and see themselves as God sees them, whether they are fourteen, forty, or eighty-two.

I wonder how many of us who choose to stay faithful to the gospel of Jesus Christ will someday say at the end of our mortal journey, "Thank you, dear Savior, for not letting me miss heaven's window. It truly was the best part of the trip."

❀ ❀ ❀

For rubies to be discovered, rocks have to be cracked and broken open; it is the only way. Only then can rocks reveal the precious treasure inside. Jesus's flesh was broken and cracked open to reveal the powerful treasure of His Atoning sacrifice. Use this treasure. The power of Christ's Atonement will set you free. You will at times feel cracked. You will sometimes feel broken. But Jesus Christ is the Rock on which you can rely to restore your wholeness and to give you peace. Make Christ the cornerstone of your self-worth. In doing so, you will not only make it to heaven's window but you will also happily sail right through it into Heavenly Father's arms.

NOTES

1 Robert Ludlum, Goodreads, http://www.goodreads.com/quotes/510196-the-most-precious-jewels-are-not-made-of-stone-but.

2 See Carrie Underwood, "Temporary Home," Arista Nashville, 2009.

3 Elaine S. Dalton, "Guardians of Virtue," *Ensign*, May 2011, 121.

4 Elaine S. Dalton, "Remember Who You Are," *Ensign*, May 2010, 120–123.

5 Dieter F. Uchtdorf, "The Reflection in the Water," CES fireside for young adults, Brigham Young University, November 1, 2009, http://www.lds.org/ldsorg/v/index.jsp?locale=0&sourceId=81e3f 5036e881210VgnVCM100000176f620a____&vgnextoid=43d 031572e14e110VgnVCM1000003a94610aRCRD.

6 Kate Fox, "Mirror, Mirror: A Summary of Research Findings on Body Image," Social Issues Research Centre, 1997, http://www.sirc. org/publik/mirror.html.

7 Julie Henry, *The Telegraph*, November 15, 2009, accessed May 12, 2012, http://www.telegraph.co.uk/lifestyle/6568552/Baby-images-airbrushed-by-magazines-to-make-them-more-perfect. html.

8 "A Return to Virtue," *Ensign*, October 2009.

9 See Jennifer Faddis, "The Skinny on Body Image," News Around the College: College of Education, University of Missouri, accessed May 12, 2012, http://education.missouri.edu/news/articles/ press-releases/PR%20Women%20of%20All%20Sizes%20

Feel%20Badly%20about%20their%20Bodies%20after%20
Seeing%20Models.php.

10 Lexie and Lindsay Kite, "Why 'Fitspiration' Isn't so Inspirational," Beauty Redefined, May 15, 2012, http://www.beautyredefined. net/why-fitspiration-isnt-so-inspirational/.

11 Lexie and Lindsay Kite, "Beauty Redefined: Rejecting the Media's Impossible Standards," *LDS Living Magazine*, January 18, 2011, http://ldsliving.com/story/63275-beauty-redefined-rejecting-the-medias-impossible-standards.

12 James E. Talmage, "The Parable of the Treasure Vault," *New Era*, February 2010, 12–13.

13 Al Fox, personal interview with author, April 5, 2013.

14 Ezra Taft Benson, "Jesus Christ—Gifts and Expectations," Brigham Young University devotional address, December 10, 1974, http://speeches.byu.edu/?act=viewitem&id=90.

15 Jeffrey R. Holland, "What I Wish Every Member Knew—and Every Longtime Member Remembered," *Ensign*, October 2006.

16 Jeffrey R. Holland, "We Want the Best for You," *New Era*, January 2010, 5.

A SPECIAL THANK YOU...

WHEN I WAS HALFWAY DONE writing this book, I received a letter from my niece Rachelle. She sent me this drawing and an offer to illustrate the cover. Her request touched me. I felt extremely humbled that she had confidence in herself and in me to publish this book. If I could choose what my cover would look like, I'd choose her drawing because it conveys the heart of what the Ruby Secret is all about: bravely believing in yourself and believing that a divine Being has entrusted you with special talents and gifts so you can accomplish your mission here on earth and gain eternal happiness. I could not ask for better cheerleaders! I may not make millions of dollars writing about virtue and self-worth and Young Women values, but that is the least of why I write. I do it because somewhere out there, there is a young girl who wants to believe she is precious. And I want more than anything to remind her that she is—by teaching her or her mother or Church leader that being precious to God is what makes us beautiful! It is what gives us worth beyond measure, and in the end, it is what makes us truly happy.

ABOUT THE AUTHOR

Jodi Marie Robinson is a wife, mother, and popular inspirational speaker. She and her husband are the parents of four children. She teaches motivational and life skills classes to women recovering from drug addiction at a treatment center in Salt Lake City. She sees firsthand how believing in a higher power, something far greater than herself, can transform a person's destiny. She enjoys serving in her Church callings, volunteering at her children's school, and doing everything she can to make the world a better place. On a side note, she can be bribed easily if chocolate is involved. Milk chocolate is her first love, but with age is coming an affinity for the dark!

Share your Ruby Secret experience with Jodi on her website. She loves hearing from her readers.

www.jodimarierobinson.webs.com
www.jodimarierobinson.blogspot.com

To schedule a fireside or other speaking arrangement, contact her at therubysecret@gmail.com.

*You are more precious than rubies and all the things thou
canst desire are not to be compared unto you.*

—PROVERB 3:15